CW01011287

THE FEEL GOOD FACTORY ON

life management

THE FEEL GOOD FACTORY ON

life management

Mind-clearing, path-finding,
change-making ways to
revitalise your life

The Feel Good Factory led by Elisabeth Wilson

MANUFACTURED BY
THE FEEL GOOD FACTORY

Copyright © Infinite Ideas Limited, 2010

First published in 2010 by
Infinite Ideas Limited
36 St Giles
Oxford
OX1 3LD
United Kingdom
www.infideas.com

A CIP catalogue record for this book is available from the British Library

ISBN 978–1–906821–41–8

Brand and product names are trademarks or registered trademarks of their
respective owners.

Designed by D.R.ink
Typeset by Nicki Averill
Printed in India

Contents

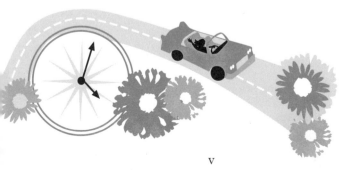

Introduction

Where are you going in life, and do you have the tools to get you there? Do you long to find purpose and *reorientate* yourself along your life's Right Path? Have you messed up and realised you've taken the Wrong Path and wish to blazes you could get off it? Or perhaps you're floundering around in the wilderness wondering where on earth that confounded Right Path has got to?

This book is for everyone who wants – needs – to put themselves back on the right track, rev up their life, seize the reins of destiny once more, and reignite their engines of enthusiasm.

Let's face it – it's easy to lose your way in the mad, crazy 24 hour consumer-driven world we live in. Too many choices, too much to do, too much to worry about – too much *stuff*.

'Buy this', 'wear that', 'become this', 'go there', 'live like them', 'have it all', 'get it all done' – and *pronto* – such is the message for twenty-first century man and woman. Little wonder we're stressed and overworked, with houses strewn with items we don't want and never use, and desperately in need of that perfect, Utopian work–life balance.

Give yourself a few minutes for a self-assessment. Ask yourself – how happy am I today? Are my relationships healthy and fulfilling? Do I get enough 'R and R' in my day? Am I in control of my life? Am I overwhelmed by clutter, nonsense, commitments – even people – I just don't want? Has life become devoid of pleasure? Am I drowning in a sea of worries? Or just plod plod plodding along the treadmill of life with no hope for the future?

Sadly, one recent survey found that only 36% of us would describe ourselves as 'very happy', and one poll found that four out of ten of us think life has become worse in recent years.

Why? One reason for our general dissatisfaction is too much work and not enough play. Nearly 70% of us complain we don't have enough time to ourselves. The International Stress Management Association says that nearly a third of us are finding it stressful to balance our work and home lives. Worse, according to the British Heart Foundation, half a million people in the UK believe that work stress may actually be making them ill.

So finding that work–life balance, simplifying life and reviewing our relationships should be a top priority; experts tell us that those who do find a satisfying work–life balance, who set aside time to relax and de-stress and spend time with those they love not only have richer lives, but are more likely to be healthier and live longer.

That's where this book comes in. It's packed with ideas to help you revitalise your life. It takes you on a journey during which you'll be encouraged to re-examine your values and give your life an MOT.

It involves some serious life (as well as health) detoxing – and that means more than just sipping lemon juice whilst wearing a white bathrobe. You may need to do some unpleasant stuff too, like discarding the unhelpful beliefs and habits that are holding you back.

In short, this book should help you to do one massive de-clutter – and not just of your stuff, but of every area of your life from your home and garden, to your finances, and even your social circle.

It's all within your grasp – and is probably easier than you think.

Andy Warhol once wrote, 'They say time changes things, but you actually have to change them yourself.'

So if you've been guilty (and haven't we all?) of hoping life will pick up without you actually kick-starting the process, then here's where the inertia ends. Remember, if you feel in control, you *are* in control.

Here's your springboard to a new life. What are you waiting for?

Feel good now: *'Vocation is where your deep gladness meets the world's great hunger, that's where you're going to find your calling.'*
Frederick Buchener, Presbyterian Minister

One
Find your focus

You want something different, you just don't know what. Finding out is vital. That's what this first section is all about.

Quiz:
Where are you right now?

So you're ready for change? Step right this way, because everything starts with you – *your* mind, *your* way of thinking, *your* life philosophy. You need to start unpicking it, scrutinising it, then give it a darned good shake – reprogramme it if you like, and then put it back where you found it, hopefully a bit clearer, wiser and certainly more focused.

It's important to remember that you can't change others, only yourself – or at least the way you behave and react to things – and then hope that those around you will adapt to the new you. And there's every chance they will.

How centred and focused are you?

To revitalise your life, you need to develop these two qualities.   Being centred suggests you are serene, fulfilled and content. Being focused enables you to reach that point. So that's what we're aiming for.

Read the paired descriptions that follow and rate how well each statement describes you by assigning a number between 1 and 7 on the following scale:

Doesn't describe me at all   *Describes me very well*

1   2   3   4   5   6   7

- I know where I'm going.
- My plans never get off the ground – events tend to work out consistently against me.

- I have a life plan – and I'm following it through.
- I find it hard to make any decisions about where I'm heading.

- I'm confident and ambitious.
- I find it hard to muster true enthusiasm for any goals or challenges.

- Things tend to go my way.
- Luck doesn't seem to be on my side.

- I am usually unflappable, energetic but in control.
- My everyday life seems lacklustre.

- I usually live in a state of calm – industrious, diligent, successful and composed.
- I'm short on vitality.

Scoring

Find out if you are classified as *focused, unfocused* or *in-between.*

When you have answered each question, you can find your 'Where I'm at' rating by subtracting your score for the second question from your score for the first question within each pair.

So if you gave 5 to the first description and 1 to the second, you would have a 'Where I'm at' score of plus 4. If however, you'd given 2 to the first description and 7 to the second, you'd have a 'Where I'm at' Score of minus 5.

3 or above – you're *focused*

-3 or below – you're *unfocused*

Any other score – you're somewhere *in-between*

Willpower – all you need to make changes

In order to make the lifestyle changes to revitalise your life, you need one magic ingredient – willpower.

Here is how you build up a mental image strong enough to motivate you. Think of your willpower as being like a karate chop. Short, sharp, effective.

When you can't be bothered to get going, see yourself decked out in a karate outfit, chopping planks of wood into splinters with your bare hands. That's the sort of decisiveness you need to muster if you're going to change long-ingrained habits that aren't helping you.

Step 1. Notice distractions

Some of us make up our minds to do something, and it's as good as done. Meanwhile, most of us have minds like kites in the wind, blown around by whatever catches our attention. If you are one of the people who are very easily distracted then becoming aware of that can help enormously. Notice when you sit down to work how you are distracted by the urgent need to know what's on TV this evening. Notice when you are distracted from that healthy salad by the siren song of the focaccia and double cheese. Notice that when you are about to start working on your

Think of your willpower as being like a karate chop

CV you are easily pulled away by the phone call from a friend. Don't do anything just yet ... only notice.

Step 2. Learn the mantra

This is your personal reminder to yourself to complete what you've started. It is a sentence you say out loud as often as you need to but most especially when you notice you are being distracted. You will have to find one that works for you but 'My intention now is to...' works for most situations. Saying it out loud is crucial.

Step 3. Get out of your comfort zone

This is the hard bit. Now you are going to prove to yourself that you're not a wuss, incapable of making the changes you want to make. Next time you're in the shower, turn the temperature control from hot to cold for one second. Each day turn the water on cold for just a bit longer. Work up gradually until you can stand under the cold water for 60 seconds. Then try an experiment; turn it down to cold for just 10 seconds. It will seem like a complete breeze. Your comfort zone has extended. You have used your willpower like a karate chop and if you can do it once you can do it again. The memory will stay with you, building your self-esteem and pushing you on to achieve other good stuff.

This seems a strange thing to do but it is a very powerful exercise. If you have tried over and over again to make changes in your life and failed, that's a big backlog of disappointment in yourself. And, let's face it, it's simply failure to achieve what you want to achieve. This cold-shower test isn't easy but it does change your idea of yourself very quickly. You soon see yourself as the sort of person who sets a goal and keeps to it. That's incredibly revitalising. As well as giving you greater belief in your ability to get things done, getting out of your comfort zone in one area makes you more interested in doing it in others. You'll become more open to new experiences, more interested in life and more open to change.

Step 4. Start small

While you are proving to yourself that a comfort zone is easily conquered, build up your confidence and belief in yourself as someone who states their intention, and follows through. Start small. Promise yourself that tomorrow you will do something simple that you can't fail at: reading your child a bedtime story; flossing your teeth; eating an apple. If you fail, pick something easier the next night. Willpower is like a muscle: the more you use it, the larger it grows. Soon you'll be keeping big promises, too.

What do you want, where are you going?

To bring about real and lasting change get into the habit of asking yourself the right questions. The right question, well formed and asked with clear intentions, will point you in the right direction.

When you master the art of asking the right questions you're more than halfway to finding your best answers. Ask yourself the right questions and coach yourself into a habit of self-questioning on a regular basis. You'll be developing questions that both put you in touch with what you really want and help in finding the best possible ways of achieving this.

Powerful questions not only change the way you think but also the choices and actions you make. You know when you've hit upon one of these questions when you think, 'Oh, I hadn't thought about it like that,' or 'That's a good question,' or words or thoughts to that effect. Questions can be used to generate new possibilities and challenge old ways of thinking and behaviours, as well as validating and encouraging progress. But when you ask the questions be prepared to listen to and take on board the answers.

Powerful questions change the choices and actions you make

To keep tabs on the kinds of questions you ask, use the following checklist as a form of accountability to ensure your questions are taking you in the right direction.

- Will making this choice take me towards what I truly want or will it keep me stuck in my past?
- Am I pleasing myself or trying to please others?
- Does thinking about taking this action make me feel energised or do I feel drained?
- Will this habit or action give me short-term gratification or will I gain longer-lasting satisfaction?
- Am I focusing on the solution or on the problem?
- Are my thoughts right now self-nurturing and affirming or self-attacking and critical?
- Will this habit or action empower me or disempower me?

Examples of questions you may ask yourself on a regular basis might include:

- What is it I really, really want?
- If I imagined that I knew what to do, the first thing I would do is…?
- What solutions can I imagine that could solve this challenge?
- In a similar situation what have I done that worked?

- If I had no choice but to make this work, what would I do differently from what I'm doing now?

Give the switching questions method a go. This method was originated by Marilee G. Adams, founder of the Center for Inquiring Leadership. Switching questions requires making the switch from the judger mindset, which focuses on problems and asks questions such as 'Why wasn't I invited?' or 'Why doesn't she like me?' to the learner mindset where the focus is on solutions, choices and what's right, and asks 'What options can I consider here?' or 'What can I learn from this?' Asking questions from the learner mindset will create more questions that focus on solutions and positive outcomes.

There will be times when a question causes you not only to pause but also to sit with it in your thoughts for a while. When this happens treat the question as an enquiry, a chance to reflect more deeply and allow the answers to emerge from inside you. Enquiring questions push your thinking below the surface of your everyday, mundane thoughts where you have greater access to deeper and more multilayered aspects of your self and personality.

A useful method is to reframe and pose the question in the context of a solution. So the question 'Why did I mess that up?' becomes 'What did I do right or what did I do well?'. 'Why am I so dumb?' reframed becomes 'What evidence do I have of my skills and strengths?'. 'Why is that person better than me?' becomes 'In what ways am I different from that person?'. Reframing is a really useful technique that will help you gain confidence and skill in devising powerful questions.

Finally, don't shy away from asking yourself the questions you'd rather not ask or be asked. You know, the kind of question that puts you on the spot or addresses an issue you would rather ignore. Bringing these questions out into the open can lead to powerful and often life-changing decisions.

Change is possible

Take some time to think about the following.

Think of someone who seems to exude 'vitality'.
1.What makes that person full of vitality?

2. Do you think that person deserves to have that kind of energy and success?

3.What do you think that person does to deserve it?

What are you grateful for in your life?
1.Would you be unhappy without these things or relationships?

2. If yes, then does it make you happy now to have them?

Think about three good things that have happened in your life.
1.What role did you play in influencing these situations?

2.What aspects of these good things were driven by you and what elements were out of your control?

What are the three most unsatisfying areas of your life right now?

1. In what way do you think you have contributed to this?

2.Would you think and behave differently if you had the chance to go back in time – how would you change things?

These should hopefully have given you some food for thought.You'll find a few more soul-searching exercises and big questions to ponder in the following chapters. Take them slowly – they're your first steps on the springboard to change.

Kyra Sedgewick's life management tips

Golden Globe award-winning actor, wife of Kevin Bacon, mother and yoga-freak on how she finds her path.

She prioritises what's really important

'I think that knowing your priorities will simplify how you draw up your to do list. When work is a priority but it's definitely below family then some things will fall into place. When you're learning lines and the phone rings and it's a friend, you make a decision about whether to let it go and keep learning the lines. When it's my daughter, I'm always going to pick up.'

She believes in a treat a day

'As far as looking after yourself, I think it's really important to do something nice for yourself every day whether it's walking down the street and getting a frozen yogurt or icecream or taking a bath.'

She believes in community

'All our fiscal worries have brought us back to keeping it simple when we want to feel good. Whether it's singing along to a song you love or bringing people together for a meal. We don't need to eat out, we can invite friends over, ask them to contribute a dish, all eat together. It wasn't until my son went to college I realised how much I treasured nights when as a family we made tacos and salad and ate together. I ache for it.'

Hit the sweet spot

Feeling under pressure to know
just what your life mission is?
Don't worry, help is at hand.

Here is a novel way of finding out what it is you really want to do with your life. Get creative, find your 'sweet spot', as it's been called, and have fun designing and fulfilling your own life purpose. You are going to ask yourself three important questions and find the place where your responses interlock and meet. That's the sweet spot.

Draw three large interlocking circles on a blank page.

- In the first circle write about your deep interests or passions, subjects you're energised and engaged by; hobbies, amateur interests, obsessions or causes you're fired up about.
- In the second circle write about the things that you enjoy doing that you know people will pay you to do – marketable skills and abilities that you've developed through your working life.
- In the third circle, write about the activities you enjoy doing that find you at your best, the things you're excellent at doing – the things you do uniquely well. In other words, the activities you'd do just because of how much you get out of doing them.

Where these circles interlock is where you'll feel fully engaged, motivated, fulfilled and joyful about your life and

your work. This is the centre of your Life Mission
or calling.

What if once you've recognised what you would like to do,
you realise that it's going to be difficult to find paid work
in that sphere? There are plenty of ways in which you
can engage your interests while working towards a more
established career in that sector. Why not start a blog?
Become a fan of bloggers who work in that area. What
about volunteering or finding a mentor who works in the
sector? Do what you can to remain connected and think
outside the box to keep those connections flowing. The
more experiences, knowledge and expertise you gain, the
stronger your position will be at a later stage. Be excited by
the possibilities and opportunities you could create.

*Think outside the box to keep
those connections flowing*

Still stuck? Take one of the activities you love doing and brainstorm the many different ways you could get paid for doing this one thing. Brainstorms work even better with a group. They'll go down a storm on nights out with your mates, with crazy and often great ideas being suggested. Share your brainstorm with strangers who won't care about censoring ideas. Run the same brainstorm for several days or even weeks, soliciting ideas wherever you go.

Motivate, recreate

It's a myth to think that you have to be in the mood to be motivated. When you know what motivates you, you'll be better equipped to call on those influences when you need them.

Here we explore some of the often-ignored elements of motivation.

Stay put

The discipline of staying put is one such often-ignored element of motivation. Regularly leaving work interrupts flow and the quality of thinking. The longer you stay put in the seat at the computer, the more motivated you become. Try it. Double or triple the amount of time you would normally allocate for a task and then stick with it.

Incentives

When it comes to motivation, incentives and bribes really help. Knowing they're going on holiday will motivate most people to get on top of their workload. The holiday serves as a short-term reward and incentive. At the same time, there's no point kidding yourself that you'll fit into a size 10 dress in six weeks' time for your sister's wedding when you're currently three dress sizes bigger. Pinpoint an area of your life where you would like to be motivated. Plan in smaller incentives that acknowledge your achievements and celebrate progress.

Incentives and bribes really help

One of the best-known motivation theories was pioneered by American clinical psychologist Frederick Herzberg in the 1930s. This became commonly known as the two-factor theory as Herzberg identified two sources of motivation. The first category was what Herzberg named the hygiene factors. Included in the list of hygiene factors were the following: having access to supervision, opportunity for positive interpersonal relationships, a good salary and a positive working environment. You might want to do what you can to bring these into your life. The second category included achievement, recognition, work, responsibility and advancement.

Get to know your supporting motivating influences

What are the criteria or conditions that influence how motivated you feel? At a basic level many people are motivated by pain to move away from what doesn't work. Think about the times in your life when things got so bad you just couldn't bear it any more. Perhaps the pain manifested itself in your own life in the breakdown of a relationship or resigning from your job. The pain motivates you to make a change. On the other hand, it might be the incentive of a reward that you find motivating and encouraging. There are many other factors that have a strong influence on levels of motivation.

- Power and authority
- Belonging and connection
- Achievement and contribution
- Rewards and incentives
- Praise and acknowledgement
- Deadlines and accountability
- Planning and being in control
- Fear of failure or fear of success
- Competition and proving yourself
- Inspiration and enthusiasm

Three of the most important social motivators are power and authority, belonging and connection, and achievement and contribution. Which of the three do you most identify with? Can you see the ways in which these motivating influences are being met in your current work and personal life right now? Acknowledging your motivating influences as needs that must be met is an important step to increasing how motivated you'll become.

Rewards and bribery

There are some tasks and projects you just won't be motivated to do. When this happens it's time to use rewards and bribery. Make a list of treats and rewards you enjoy giving yourself. Now make a list of tasks you feel unmotivated about tackling. Match one of your treats or rewards with each of the tasks you feel unmotivated to complete. Now take each item on this list one by one. You want to make sure that the treat or bribe is enough to get you going. When you read out the task and the treat that you'll be rewarding yourself with, notice if it resonates with a big Yes. If it's not a match, either replace the reward or bribe with a new one or up your offer. When it feels like a definite Yes, move on to the next item on your list.

Micro managing to beat procrastination

Approaching your work and tasks by taking small steps and applying minute incremental actions works particularly well when you have a tendency to procrastinate, are feeling stressed or overwhelmed or if you're a perfectionist.

A micro movement is a very tiny action that's five seconds to five minutes long. A ten-second task is far easier to carry out than one that we know might take us five hours.

Draw an empty circle and write the name of the project or task you need to complete in the centre (it's a good idea to choose one you've been avoiding). Divide your circle into several sections and label each section with the micro movement that needs to be taken. Date and time each movement, which can be changed. Work on one micro movement at a time. Prove a point and complete one of your micro movements in the next five minutes.

Feel good now: *'Much of the day should be in a strict sense idle, for it is often in idle moments that real inspiration comes.'*

John Updike, novelist

Reinvent your life

Does it feel like time to change direction?
Would you like to set yourself new challenges
and start afresh? If you could start all over
again, what might be your first step?

Using these four easy steps you'll learn how to coach yourself through the journey of making the move from where you are to where you want to be. Making this choice is about stepping out big and not hiding your light under a bushel. You're letting the world know that these are the changes you've made and this is what the new you stands for.

Use the following 4 'R' model from start to finish.

The 4 Rs of reinvention

1. Research. Do your research. You can always spot the person who has invested time in doing this. What they have to offer has freshness and crispness to it. Have you gone out and interviewed three people working in the field you're interested in moving into? Have you done any shadowing? Send an email to someone working in the field or industry you'd love to learn more about. Outline who you are, what prompted your request and what you would like to explore and find out about in three days of shadowing them. Keep it short and concise.

2. Release. Make your move as clean and smooth as possible. That means paying attention to the ways in which you leave and say goodbye. Make sure you've tied up all loose ends and had closure. You could give away all your books on a subject you are no longer

interested in. Or all the clothes that no longer fit in with your self-image (of course, you have to decide first on what your new self-image will be, which is good fun in its own way). Don't just stick to objects. Ask the don't-want-to-ask question: 'what beliefs do I need to release?' Doing this work first will make the reinvention a smoother transition.

3. Reaffirm. You may be letting go of old skills and areas of knowledge, values and beliefs. But which of these qualities will you be taking with you? There is no need to throw out the baby with the bathwater. Make a point of reaffirming the strengths and skills, values and beliefs (positive ones) that you'll still be using. Making a conscious effort to identify and acknowledge your skills and resources is another important step as you make the transition.

4. Reinvent. How will you stand out from the crowd? Take a look at who's out there leading in the field or profession you wish to move into. What can you learn from them? This is not about being competitive. This is about appreciating the successes of those who are leading and learning from them. What services, products and skills will it be important for you to embrace? Think also about the value you bring. Make your mark not just with your business or career but also in your appearance.

Faking it

Want to know the fastest way to become the person you want to be. Fake it!

Right now you probably believe you don't have what
it takes to achieve your dreams – or let's face it, you'd
already be there. Let's say you lack the confidence to step
into a role or career you really have the experience to do.
Perhaps you long to be a manager and the opportunity has
come up to cover for maternity leave but you find yourself
reluctant to apply. That's when you apply the techniques
of faking it. Don't get me wrong – we're not talking about
going to extremes here and lying. Faking it works when
you have either the qualifications or the experience or both
but just don't have the belief you can do it.

Faking it isn't being an imposter; but it does push you
out of your comfortable and familiar territory into an
uncomfortable one. What's really being suggested is that
you step up your game.

Researchers at the University of Wake Forest, North
Carolina, asked a group of fifty students to act like
extroverts for 15 minutes in a group even if they didn't
feel like it. The more assertive and energetic they were, the
happier they felt. The thing is that at some point we've all
faked it; it's legitimate whether it's the first day, week or in
some cases months of a new job (not so much perhaps if
you're someone who's paid to save people's lives). But for

the better part of the time there's room for not knowing, practising and making mistakes, taking your time to take on responsibility and learning
the ropes.

Remember that confidence comes after the act, not before. Please make this your mantra. When you have a new post, your job will be to learn from your mistakes and to succeed in the areas of your strengths and talents. You will rise to the challenge once you have found yourself out of your depth.

To stretch yourself into faking it, why not try the following:

- Go for a position three steps ahead of where you already are. Expose yourself to that environment. Even sending for an application form or updating your CV can push you into acting and thinking differently.
- Take on something bigger than you've ever tackled. You could start a festival, or organise a market, or arrange a group meeting in your area. Being treated as the person who makes all the decisions is in itself enough to get you thinking of yourself in a new way.
- How you look can play a large part in how you feel and act. What about adding a scarf or a tie or in fact doing the opposite and taking them away? Is there an

accessory that could be updated to give you a whole new look? Changing your hairstyle is one of the oldest ways of signalling a change. Don't forget your feet. Shoes say a lot about you. Would a new pair of shoes stand you on more solid ground? How does your new look feel? Are there more changes still to be made?

If you pretend to be confident for long enough, eventually you will begin not only to feel confident but also to be confident. It works for many in Alcoholics Anonymous: thousands are encouraged to imagine themselves sober and to stay sober with the help of the programme. Don't forget to give yourself a pat on the back. Faking it will mean taking risks and swimming for a while in unfamiliar waters. But you can do it.

Faking it works when you don't have the belief

Future perfect

Next stop: your future life. Have serious fun creating a compelling vision for your future that's creative and inspiring. Your future lies in your hands.

Follow the advice here and you should be having more fun, feeling more creative and gaining the sense that you are getting 'into the flow'. This exercise will help take you to a whole new level because while you're being creative you are also planning your future life – brilliantly.

Go to an art or stationery shop and purchase a large sheet of poster paper (as big as 8 A4 sheets of paper) and some glue. Gather together a range of magazines from health and lifestyle women's magazines and home and garden magazines. It's important if you're buying them off the shelf to make sure they have the sort of images that appeal to you. Now set aside an hour or more. Clear a space in a room and get everything out. Make sure you're wearing comfortable clothing so you can move around easily. You're going to make a collage of your future. Start off by leafing through the magazines and tearing out images, words and ideas that move and inspire you. You don't have to worry about why you've been inspired but it might get you thinking about what areas of your life you would like that image to reflect. As you relax into the exercise you'll build up momentum. When you're doing your collage you'll probably experience what psychologists call the 'flow', being totally involved in an activity and totally focused on what you are doing in the present moment. Once you have a pile of images, start putting together your collage, using the images to reflect how you would like your life to be in the future.

Think big, think outside the box and push your own expectations about what is really possible for you. One quite startling result of making your 'vision board' is that sometime in your future you'll look at it and discover that a great deal of it has already come true.

The next step is often overlooked and yet it is an important one. What you do with your collage does make a difference. Hang it up somewhere so that you can see it regularly and be inspired by it to live towards your dream.

Push your own expectations

Two

Streamline your life

If you want to make changes, you need to find the time to do the things you want to do. So now that you have more idea of what you want, here's how to jettison what you don't.

Quiz:
How do you find more time?

Below are four groups of statements. Tick any statement that describes you (you can tick as many as you like).

A

☐ My work space is pretty messy.

☐ I spend a lot of time looking for things I need.

☐ I work on several tasks in one morning.

B

☐ Leaving things until the last possible minute feels very familiar to me.

☐ I spend a lot of time getting together the tools I need for a job and 'tidying' my space so that I'm ready to work.

☐ I am easily distracted from a task.

C

- ☐ I'm organised but I never seem to get everything done.
- ☐ I'm frustrated by having to depend on other people.
- ☐ I seem to get more anxious about deadlines than other people do.

D

- ☐ I get distracted by other people's demands and agendas.
- ☐ I often find myself saying yes when I know I should say no.
- ☐ I feel like I get stuck with the jobs that no one else wants to do.

Did you tick more answers in one group than the others? Whether you are definitely one group or a mixture of two or more, you'll find some solutions in this section.

Mostly A

You are a maverick. Subconsciously you feel that you are bucking the system and being your own person but it means you are less than productive. Time to get organised and streamline your time management skills.

Mostly B

You're a procrastinator. You don't have enough time because you find it hard to get started. You need to learn to just do it.

Mostly C

You're a perfectionist. You can't let things go but this leads to you never getting finished and sometimes never getting started.

Mostly D

You're a people pleaser. You're so busy servicing others' needs that you never get on with what you have to do. Time to get ruthless.

Do less,
achieve more

Want to know how to free up valuable minutes in your day? You can't increase the number of hours in a day, but you can get more from the time that you have by changing the way you use it.

Are you faced with too much to do and not enough time? Then start looking at your world in a different way. These simple approaches can save you hours. But you have to apply them rigorously.

Track your time

Try tracking if you're often late or miss appointments. Over the course of one day time as many of your daily activities as possible. Tracking your time may quickly reveal some startling truths. You may discover you spend three hours checking emails rather than one.

Hire in help

Ever had the feeling that your to-do list is never ending? The volume of routine tasks on your to-do list may seem harmless but these tasks steal time from the important things. If you could afford it, what activities would you pay someone else to do? Is there a way to start with the most inexpensive activity and hire someone straight away? Can any of your tasks be delegated? Or is there a need to make a decision to stop doing the activity altogether?

Mobilise the time you have

This is particularly important when you have a limited amount of time to complete an action. Have you had plenty of time to meet a deadline and found yourself distracted and wasting time? Or maybe you're up against a tight deadline to get a task completed that would, on a normal day, take double or triple the amount of time? Suddenly you're on top of it. You pull out all the stops and in the time you have the job gets done. You've just experienced what time management gurus refer to as Parkinson's Law. It can be used in both scenarios by setting aside a certain amount of time that you stick to while you concentrate your focus and get the task completed in the allocated slot of time.

Cut it out

Put yourself on a media fast and reclaim the valuable minutes and hours lost throughout your week. Fast for as little as an hour or for up to 24 hours or more. No need to go cold turkey. Simply decide what media you will take a break from. Will it be television, radio, texts, emails, the Internet, the computer, reading subscribed mail-outs, newspapers or magazines? The good news is that your fast can be broken and restarted when and as you like. Use the time gained to focus on activities and tasks that really matter. Or just simply relax.

Strategic deceit

This is very useful when it's a challenge to schedule in 'me time'. Fabricating self-imposed meetings and appointments in your diary is another way of saving time. Writer Heather Sellers calls this 'strategic deceit'. It's not the same as lying but is a method used to create time that you wouldn't normally allow yourself to have. What harm would it really do to schedule a meeting so that you can take an uninterrupted lunch break on the way back to the office? You're more likely to give yourself permission to make time for yourself when you've scheduled it in your diary in the same way that you schedule in appointments for clients and other people.

Intelligent neglect

Less time on the Internet or your mobile (even small chunks of time) lowers stress and allows time for reflective thinking and solution solving. Taking time to think increases both productivity and efficiency. In the time management world taking time off from technology is known as the practice of 'intelligent neglect'. It includes regular periods of switching your mobile to voicemail, going through your inbox and unsubscribing from mailing lists and checking emails only once or twice a day.

Shorten your to-do list

Ever thought of making a shorter to-do list? Each week pick twenty things you need to do for the rest of the week and each night write down no more than three to five actions that you want to accomplish the next day. Achieving five out of five is more satisfying than five out of twenty. You'll probably always get most things done and even end up with the possibility of doing more. Any other completed actions from the remaining fifteen items become an added bonus.

What activities would you pay someone else to do?

Free up your time

Can you find fifteen minutes in your day that
would count as free time? If the answer is no then
you need to do something about it right now.

Does the idea of having free time feel like a double-edged sword? We dream and talk obsessively about it and then when we get it we either twiddle our thumbs or find ourselves filling the space with some other mindless activity.

This is really not doing ourselves any favours. It's in our free time that we recreate ourselves. Literally. By resting we allow our unconscious mind to come up with some of our best ideas.

Many people treat free time as a reward for hard work. But instead train yourself to think of your free time as a necessary, preventative activity rather than a reward. Free time is one way to build reserves, generate ideas and solutions and to get into a frame of mind where you can access some of your best thinking. You'll not only need lots of free time that is connected to rewards but also free time that is firmly fixed to healthy well-being. Don't wait until you're burnt out to bring free time into the centre of your schedule.

Booking free time as you would any other appointment in your diary is one way of protecting your free time and ensuring that it happens. Make free time a priority by scheduling free time first, before any of your other appointments. That way your free time doesn't get tacked on the end somewhere with the likelihood of it being bounced off the schedule by other pressing engagements. Not only that but you've immediately sent yourself the message that putting this time first in your diary means that it's really important to you.

You might need to do something more to establish this appointment as unmoveable in your schedule. Time management coach Mark Forster suggests tricking the reactive mind by lying to it. This is possible because the reactive mind can't tell when the rational mind is lying. So you could say something to yourself like, 'I'm only going to do nothing for five minutes.' That way you take the first step even though you have two hours scheduled into your diary. The first step will be less of a threat to the reactive mind so it won't resist. Next thing you know, your two hours have flown by.

Take a look back over your schedule for the last six weeks and note down the last time you took a couple of hours out to do precisely nothing. You may be looking at your diary and thinking 'well, there was plenty of time but I got nervous and filled the space with more pointless tasks'. If that's the case, try putting structure to your free time until you get used to the process. Spend ten minutes meditating, going off on a ten-minute mindful walk or spend ten minutes writing in your notebook. It might seem like it's going against the grain but these activities will ground and support you to make the most of your free time whenever you have it.

Another way to get used to the idea is to find room for growth – literally. Everyone deserves a room of their own. But it doesn't need to be an actual room. It could be your car; it could be in the pages of your journal. When he first came to London, poet, novelist and broadcaster Benjamin Zephaniah's room was a bench on a roundabout in Stratford where he would sit and watch the world go by as he figured out how to sort out his life. Whether in public or private, mark out a room of your own and schedule in a time to visit it in the next seven days.

Put a time frame on time spent doing nothing. Sticking to your allotted time lessens the possibility of procrastination. So a twenty minute break has its place in your day but doesn't turn into a whole day away from your task. Very often entering a space of having nothing to do actually brings to mind all the things that we're unhappy about or perhaps avoiding. In other words we tap into worry and anxiety. The simplest and easiest thing you can do when these feelings arise is to close your eyes and take several really deep breaths.

As thoughts enter your mind (which they will do) instead of judging them and pushing them away allow them to rise and fall away as you focus your concentration on your breathing. The idea is not to push your thoughts away but to follow their flow and let them go. Just a few minutes of this practice can be remarkably calming time.

Think of your free time as a necessary activity

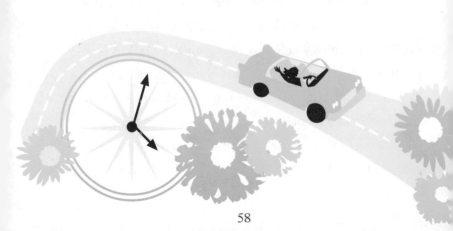

Join the Slow Movement

Slow is the practice of taking one thing at a time. What about dedicating a day in your week to a slow activity? You could take off your watch for the duration of your activity; for example, take your time reading a good book curled up on the sofa, read a whole book to a small child, take a long uninterrupted bath, cook a slow soup or casserole, take a long slow walk through nature or around your neighbourhood, start a 1,000 piece jigsaw puzzle, eat dinner or lunch without any rush or – for those lucky ones – finish off your day with some slow love making (or do it in the middle of the day). Choose one idea and slowly enjoy it from start to finish.

Eliminate what drains you

One of the easiest ways to feel instantly energised is the simple process of removing tolerations (things and people that drain your energy) from your life.

In coaching the word 'toleration' is generally applied to areas of your life where you're putting up with something without realising the cost to yourself in terms of energy, wasted time spent worrying and inconvenience.

Tolerations can include unfinished projects, incomplete household chores (things that either need fixing or replacing) and relationships that, when examined, leave you feeling drained. On closer examination you'll find that tolerations – whether physical, emotional or mental – drain your energy and distract you from the important tasks that will take you in the direction of success.

Take a good look at your life and make a list of key areas where you might be putting up with tolerations, for example home, relationships, work, health and well-being. Brainstorm as many items, from the small to the big, under each category. Once you have generated several items under each category, decide on where to start and get to work on clearing these tolerations as quickly as you can.

What are you putting up with in your relationships? Who are you putting up with? Which friends drain your energy and take up time? Maybe it's closer to home. What are you tolerating in your intimate relationship? Get to work on clearing these relationships too.

Keep working through your list over the next few weeks and months. It's also a good idea to get into the habit of handling your tolerations on a regular basis. With your tolerations out of the way you'll attract better opportunities because you will have cleared space for what you want in your life. So get cracking.

Tolerations drain your energy and distract you

Letting go to move forward

Sometimes in order to gain focus and achieve what we want, we need to cut out activities.

What's the one thing you could stop doing that would make a difference to your productivity? If you can work out the things to let go of, you'll get better at knowing what to focus on.

This idea will be useful to you if you find that every time you write a to-do list, it's a waste of time. As soon as you strike off one task, another three spring to mind to be answered. This is a sign that your current systems aren't working; so what can you do?

People who start working with a personal coach often find that rather than extending the list of things they want to do, the list of things to *stop* doing actually increases. The focus becomes prioritising what really matters. Instead of taking on more projects and challenges it is more important to let things go and achieve clarity on what your priorities will be.

Take a moment and close your eyes for a few seconds. Think about all the activities you do in your day. As you scan the list try to identify which activities feel draining or give you that feeling of 'That's such a drag to do'. When that feeling or thought comes up notice it and write it down. If you stopped emailing for a day, would everything really go to pot? When I asked myself that question I realised I didn't want to spend my time responding to emails. I wanted to be writing articles, carrying out research and being a lot more creative. I was always busy, but busy on the wrong things.

If you find a great idea that you want to achieve, before you get to work on it, decide on the one thing you could stop doing that would give you more time and energy to focus on your goal.

Here are a couple of questions for you. What will be the one thing you'll stop doing and what goal or action will this allow you to focus on? Focusing on one thing at a time is the way successful people have always done things. You might be busy but you also might be sabotaging your success.

Remember that we all have so many options and choices nowadays, that we need to start saying no to some of the good things in order to accommodate the best things.

Get better at knowing what to focus on

Isabella Rossellini's life management tips

The beautiful former model and cult actress is now retraining as a film maker.

She follows her passion

'My parents always told me, "If you follow your heart and do what you like, there's a better chance that that is where your talent lies." I should have listened to them. I'm 57 years old. Better late than never.'

She looks to the positive

'The first question is always "What do you do to stay young?". I do nothing. Yes, my face has wrinkles. But I don't find it monstrous. I'm so surprised that the emphasis on ageing is on physical decay when ageing brings such incredible freedom. Now what I want most is laughs. I just want to laugh.'

She keeps finding new focus

'When my youngest child was 14 I thought "My children don't need me in the same way. I'm not modelling any more and I act, but in fewer leading roles. Maybe it's time to go back to school." The big "aha" about growing older is the mental freedom. I'm older than my teachers. It's fantastic – I was always afraid of teachers but now I'm not.'

Revamp your to-do list

To-do lists are essential for most of us but they can be a huge drain on energy.

The list that never seems to get any shorter is not so much an aide-memoire as a horrible reminder that we're running fast but getting nowhere. And what could be more dispiriting than that? The other side, of course, is that to-do lists are incredibly useful tools for motivating us and making us more productive. Having a clear plan for the day ahead focuses the mind and puts you in control like nothing else. Whether you're a CEO, freelance, stay-at-home parent or student, the well run to-do list will give you a sense of full-capacity living.

But for it to work you have to have a definite system. Try this one. It is based on the advice given to 1930s magnate Charles Schwabb by a young man he challenged to double his (Schwabb's) productivity. The young man told him to write down the six most crucial tasks for each day in order of importance and work down the list. Then teach his staff to do the same. After a few weeks, the story goes that Schwabb sent the man a cheque for $25,000, which was a huge sum back then.

The idea works on the principle that we put off the important stuff (or we work to others' agendas so we don't get round to what's important for us) and keep ourselves busy with lesser tasks to distract ourselves. But if we don't do the one important thing, no matter what we achieve we'll feel dissatisfied at the end of the day. Instead of an abstract list of things to do that you attack randomly, switch the angle from what you *must* do to when you are *going* to do it.

Put this into practice

In your diary or a separate notebook, draw a line down the left hand side of the page to form a column and mark in the working hours of the day. This can be precise (9.30, 10.30, etc.) or loose (morning, early afternoon). Now you're set to go.

- At the end of your working day, brew a cuppa, sit for a second, take a deep breath and gather your thoughts. Pat yourself on the back for what you have achieved today. Then swing your mind forward into tomorrow.
- Ask yourself what regular scheduled tasks or meetings you have for tomorrow. Block them off on your diary page.
- Remember to add in travelling time, lunch and relaxation.
- What is your major task? What must you do tomorrow? That gets priority and should be done first thing if

possible. Set aside a realistic block of time (err on the side of caution). Be precise.

- Put in specific times for phone calls/emails. It is more time effective to do these in two or three blocks rather than breaking concentration and doing it ad hoc during the day.
- What's your next most important task? Is there room in your day? If you have time left, you can schedule in another task, but be realistic.
- For each week have a short list of brief one-off tasks (phone calls, paying bills, birthday cards) and if you have a few down moments, slot them in.

Having a clear plan puts you in control

Turn off to power through

Switch off your mobile for as long as you can comfortably get away with it, but aim for at least an hour in the morning and an hour in the afternoon. These should be your high productivity times when you aim to really motor through your tasks. The action of switching off your mobile sends an unconscious message to your brain that this is time when your interests are the priority, and it helps to focus your mind on the task at hand.

Stop acting on impulse

If you've ever bought something and then regretted it almost immediately, then read on. You'll learn how to save money by avoiding impulse purchases.

There's a Marx Brothers' film in which Groucho Marx is hired to run a hotel. On arrival, he makes an announcement to the staff, which goes something like this: 'There are going to have to be some changes around here. From now on, if guests ask for a three-minute egg, give them a two-minute egg; if they ask for a two-minute egg, give them a one-minute egg; and if they ask for a one-minute egg, give them the chicken and tell them to work it out for themselves.'

Maybe Groucho's motives are questionable but he did manage to hint at today's retail world in which speed of delivery and instant gratification have become the norm. There's an episode of *The Simpsons* where a gigantic new deep fryer is being installed. Perhaps you remember the following exchange.

Shop owner: It can fry a whole buffalo in 40 seconds. Homer: (wailing voice) Oh, I want it now!

We want better quality, we want cheaper prices and, above all, we want it more or less immediately. 'Now' is becoming the only acceptable delivery time. There's physiological evidence to suggest that going on a spending spree gives us a short-term high. We actually enjoy buying stuff. Just as we're prone to comfort eat to cheer ourselves up and to allay anxiety, so comfort spending is a path to retail orgasm. We've all done it. There we are wandering through a department store and we see *it. It* could be a TV, a pair of shoes, a DVD but it's a must-have. Chances are that until you saw it you didn't even know that it existed. But now you've seen it you want it – badly. You know you're a bit short this month but you reach for your plastic chum and it's yours.

Feels good doesn't it? The weird thing is, of course, that a few weeks down the line that must-have doesn't always seem quite so necessary to your life. If you've ever thought to yourself that you have a wardrobe full of clothes and nothing to wear, chances are that you've done this many times.

So how do you save money and reduce the clutter in your home? From now on, every time you come across an item that you would normally be tempted to splash out on and which costs a significant amount (you decide what's significant) hold back. Go home and put it on your 28-day list. Make a note of the item, the date you saw it and the cost. If after 28 days you revisit your list and still think it would be a good buy, then consider acquiring it. If you do buy it, the heightened anticipation of finally getting your hands on it after a wait of 28 days or more is quite something. Still not sure? Put it back on the list for another 28 days.

Still not convinced the 28-day list is a good idea? Try this. Check how much you spent on your credit card last month. Take that out in cash and use the cash instead of the credit card this month to purchase non-essentials. How does it feel to use highly visible cash? It can be quite a shocking way to discover just how much you get through. Using real rather than virtual money will help focus your mind wonderfully.

Clear your space, clear your head

Get rid of your clutter and you're free to redefine yourself. Life becomes a lot simpler.

De-cluttering is addictive and it's life affirming. Nothing makes you feel so serene and in control of your life, so fast.

Why? Most of us live amongst piles of ancient magazines, defunct utensils and clothes that neither fit nor suit us. The Chinese believe that all these unlovely, unwanted things lying about haphazardly block the flow of energy – the chi – in our homes. Lose them and you lose a ton of guilt – guilt that you'll never fit into those hellishly expensive designer jeans again, guilt that you spent all that money on skis when you've only been skiing once in the last decade, guilt that you never cook those fabulous dinners in those two dozen cook books. You get the point. Just about everything in your home probably engenders some sort of guilt. Cut your belongings by 80% and you'll do the same to your guilt.

Why 80%? Do you know about the Pareto Principle? Take a look through your wardrobe. How many of the items in your wardrobe do you actually wear? According to the Pareto Principle you wear 20% of your wardrobe and the other 80% hangs about uselessly most of the time. The Pareto principle applies to everything: for instance, 80% of your working day is probably paperclip chasing; 20% is when you do the magic and earn your salary. But for our purposes, let's stick to the clutter: 80% of your kitchenware gathers dust; 20% gets the job done. What's the betting you'll only touch 20% of your books or CDs again. Could you bear to lose them? Risk it. Choose five items right now that you haven't worn, played or read for over a year and put them in a bag for the charity shop. You are probably feeling better already.

'Useful or beautiful, useful or beautiful' – that's the mantra. If any single object doesn't fulfil one of these criteria, bin it. Cultivate ruthlessness. If you haven't worn it, used it or thought about it in a year, do you really need it?

Have three bin bags to hand as you work: one for stuff to chuck out, one for stuff to give away to charity; one for stuff that needs mending or cleaning. Give yourself two weeks to tackle the clean and mend bag or it goes to charity, too. Something neither useful nor beautiful, but that you don't want to get rid of for sentimental reasons? Put it away for a year. Time out of sight makes it easier to get rid of things when you get them out again.

Do this little but often. Try a couple of one hour sessions per week. Try the 40–20 rule: 40 minutes graft followed by 20 minutes self-congratulatory gloating. De-cluttering gets easier with practise, soon it will be second nature.

Find a home for everything you own that is useful or beautiful. You're allowed one drawer as a glory hole for all those odd things you can't think where to put. Now (deep breath), doesn't that feel better?

Just about everything in your home probably engenders some sort of guilt

Virtual de-cluttering

The contemplation phase can help those who find de-cluttering hard. In whatever room of your home you are in right now, start looking around and dividing the items mentally into one of the following categories – virtually sorting it.

- *I love this item and really need it – keep it.*
- *I don't love it and really don't need this item any more – throw it away.*
- *I'm not sure how I feel about this item and I'm not sure that I really need it – add to maybe pile.*
- *I definitely don't love this item but I do need it – upgrade with a new replacement that you love.*

Beginning to see every item you touch as being in one of these groups can get you to the place where you can let go of things very fast indeed. It also helps when you're shopping and can stop you coming home with stuff that you're not absolutely sure that you want.

Three

Take control

You know what you want and you've cleared
space in your life so that you can go after it.
But that sense of exhilaration won't last if you
don't put some of the big stuff in place. Health,
money, image – if you don't get on top of these
things they can really drag you down. However,
when you start feeling better about these areas,
life will get much sweeter and the self-belief
generated by looking after yourself begins to
seep into other parts of your life like your career
and relationships.

Quiz:
How much do you respect your body?

The aim of the following questionnaire is to encourage you to do some proper soul-searching about how much respect you have for that body of yours, and start you thinking about what you can do today to stay younger and have a healthier tomorrow.

Read the following questions and answer true or false to each:

1. I get at least seven hours sleep a night at least five days a week. True ☐ False ☐

2. When it comes to snacking, I'm more likely to have fruit and nuts than crisps or chocolate. True ☐ False ☐

3. I exercise for at least half an hour three days a week.
True ☐ False ☐

4. I take a multivitamin/supplement every day.
True ☐ False ☐

5. I get lots of relaxation every day – meditation, yoga, taking time out is really good for the stress levels.
True ☐ False ☐

6. My parents are still fighting fit and/or lived to a ripe old age. True ☐ False ☐

7. I know what my cholesterol levels are … I get them checked. True ☐ False ☐

8. (Women) – I'm up to date with all my smear tests.
True ☐ False ☐

9. (Men) I'm not too embarrassed to check my testicles regularly. True ☐ False ☐

10. I get at least five portions of fruit and veg a day.
True ☐ False ☐

11. I regularly give my liver a rest – alcohol free days are a must. True ☐ False ☐

12. My body fat percentage is within healthy limits. True ☐ False ☐

13. I try not to eat red meat more than a couple of times a week – and stick to fish or poultry. True ☐ False ☐

14. I don't say no to the odd indulgence, but fortunately I'm the kind of person who knows when to stop. True ☐ False ☐

15. I always have my regular dental check up. True ☐ False ☐

16. If I need to shift pounds, I tend to do it slowly and steadily – I'm not a binge eater and would never starve myself. True ☐ False ☐

17. I drink 6 to 8 glasses of water a day – more when I'm exercising/drinking alcohol. True ☐ False ☐

18. I'm mindful of my fat intake – I keep it within healthy limits and make sure I get plenty of omega 3 in my diet. True ☐ False ☐

19. I get my blood pressure checked regularly – and it's within healthy limits. True ☐ False ☐

20. I do everything I can to stay as healthy as possible. True ☐ False ☐

Award yourself one point for each time you answer 'True' to a question.

17–20 points

Sounds like you're as au fait with good health and nutrition as a person can be. You could well be vegan, teetotal and never binge on anything more decadent than alfafa sprouts. Don't forget that moderation is enough when it comes to health – stressing out when your lifestyle is forced to slip a bit won't win you friends or make life straightforward. But then again, you should live longer, so I suppose you get the last laugh…

10–17 points

Chances are your intentions are good – you're eating well, exercising regularly-ish, and it appears you do strive to stay on the right side of healthy. As long as your good, healthy habits outweigh the bad, you'll be winning. But remember, the key is to find a balance between saintly and sinful behaviour. Look at the quiz answers where you obviously picked the wrong one and start focusing on the areas that could use some work. Read on for some more ideas.

10 or under

Dear, oh dear, oh dear. Party animal and kebab eater you may be, but remember, it's easy to believe you're immortal when you're a youngster. The truth is, sooner or later you've got to wise up to the benefits of drinking plenty of water, getting those health checks done, waking up to the power of flavonoids and statins, and welcoming into your lifestyle all those elements which will help keep you in rude health well into your twilight years. Start at the top of the quiz and try to embrace each of these points. Just a couple could make a huge difference to your health and life plan. Read on for some more ideas.

Take control of your health: transform the way you eat

You are what you eat. Which is the reason so many of us feel like rubbish.

The truth is very few people eat enough good quality food to stay healthy, much less have enough energy to live a happy life. Follow the basic rules of nutrition and you will almost certainly start to feel better almost immediately.

All foods are equal in one way. They are broken down for fuel, but your body can use some of that fuel more easily than others. The sources the body finds it easiest to access are: fruit, vegetables, wholegrain bread, pasta and rice because these are easiest to convert into glucose. Glucose combines with oxygen in the cells to become ATP (adenosine triphosphate), which is stored and used as needed. If this carries on normally all is well and we have enough energy; when this goes wrong, we are lacking in energy.

There are three ways that the energy supply can be disrupted:

1. Energy production is powered by vitamins – in particular the B vitamins and coenzyme Q10. B vitamins are relatively easy to get in the diet, but our ability to take up coenzyme Q10 diminishes as we get older. These nutrients are also destroyed by alcohol or smoking.

2. Without oxygen, the glucose can't be used by the cells. Poor respiration, poor circulation and damaged blood cells (anaemia) all affect our energy levels.

3. Some carbohydrates are too effective at creating energy. Refined carbs such as pasta, white bread and doughnuts are converted so quickly that if the body's given a huge dose of them – and let's face it, that's how it often gets these foods – it gets overexcited, panics and stores the sugar – and these stores are what make us fat. Our bodies are really good at this because those whose ancestors weren't good at it didn't tend to make it through times of famine.

So how do you use this information? Follow these rules. They are simple but don't underestimate how difficult it is to change habits, especially when it comes to food. Take it one step at a time.

The best piece of advice on changing eating habits is one that numerous nutritionists have given me – don't think of cutting out; instead focus on adding in.

A six-week plan to transform your eating habits

Each week concentrate on adding in one habit. You can do them all at once but, if you find eating regularly and well difficult, take it one week at a time.

1. Eat breakfast every day. No excuses.

2. Eat lunch every day. No excuses.

3. Start snacking. Never go longer than three hours without eating. Regular healthy snacks mean you don't overeat at mealtimes. Eating large amounts at mealtimes also depletes your energy so you might feel on more sparkling form with smaller, more manageable meals.

4. Add in energy-giving carbs. Eat a fist-sized portion of wholegrain carbohydrate at every meal because it supplies B vitamins and doesn't get broken down too fast; for instance, wholegrain pasta, brown rice, oats or wholemeal bread (around two slices). Wholegrains contain fibre and fibre slows down the release of the sugars in carbs into the bloodstream. This means constant energy.

5. Add in energy-giving protein. Eat a deck of cards-sized portion of protein at lunch and if you really want to see a difference in your energy levels, have some at breakfast too. That means meat, fish, eggs, cottage cheese, tofu.

6. Drink enough fluid – about one to two litres a day – not including alcohol or strongly caffeinated drinks.

This gives you a lot of flexibility in what you eat and the best advice when trying to change your diet is to remember that it is very hard to do, and is best done gradually. Children need exposure to a new food about 20 times before they like it; the same might be true of you.

Never go longer than three hours without eating

Take control of your energy levels: move that body!

Do you feel tired a great deal of the time?
Do you need a couple of coffees to start
functioning in the morning? Is the only time
you feel energised when you're worried,
nervy or tense?

That's not normal. What is normal is for your body to move. Regular exercise can make you feel marvellous – strong, empowered and ready for anything.

How does it do this? When you run for a bus, your heart beats faster and more blood rushes around your body. You need more oxygen, so your lungs start to work faster. The essential transfer of oxygen into your cells, and carbon dioxide from your cells, happens at a faster rate. Inside your cells, the mitochondria (energy factories) are producing ATP, your body's fuel. It's produced from glucose. When we run out of glucose in the cells, our body starts producing ATP from reserves held in the fat cells of the body – literally burning fat. The more ATP you produce the better your body gets at doing it. By exercising you train your body to get better at burning off fat.

What happens without that boost of oxygen to the cells? Without the stimulus to produce more ATP, our bodies become sluggish and lethargic. If we're not getting the boost from oxygen, we start relying on other things that raise our heart rate in order to get an energy surge to carry us through the day – notably stimulants like caffeine and nicotine.

Exercise's benefits to your body are legion, but when it comes to energy, it means you will have a constant flow of energy to achieve everything you need to achieve easily and calmly. Your dependence on artificial stimulants will diminish. Your concentration will also be more focused. According to a study in the journal *Medicine and Science in Sports and Exercise*, the physically fit scored highest on memory and intelligence tests and were more creative.

But despite the research we don't see it this way. One of the problems with exercise is that we see it as something that drains away our vitality rather than something which enhances it. Exercise is one of the first things to go under pressure. In fact, it should be one of our priorities. When we're stressed we produce adrenaline and exercise burns it off allowing us to calm down and deal with the pressure.

If you want to feel better, calmer and bang full of energy, going to the gym once every two weeks won't do it. You need to move a little much of the time. The current minimum guidelines for health are that you should include moderate activity for 30 minutes a day, 5 or 6 days a week. That would be for optimum health. You don't need to do that much at first to feel better. Just a little movement will have a great effect on your mood and attitude and will encourage you to do more.

A three-step plan to get you moving

1. Every day – let your body out to play

Movement is play for your body. Every day give it a little of what it needs to be happy. It doesn't matter if walking up the stairs is as much as you can manage: walk up the stairs today. And tomorrow aim to walk up the stairs twice. Or try a few stretches while you're watching TV. Or race your kids to the end of the street. Or join them on the trampoline for a quick bounce. Start small and build up the expectation that you will move every day – just as you would brush your teeth.

2. Every second day – feel your heart beating

Exercise that doesn't set your heart beating fast is still good for you but to start the energy-boosting process, you want to feel your heart beat, which means your lungs expand. This is cardiovascular exercise – and it includes walking, running, cycling, swimming and dancing. It doesn't include most forms of yoga, weight lifting or Pilates.

If you are not used to exercise or have been run down, walking briskly for just five minutes a day is enough to aim for at first.

3. Keep going for six weeks

For most of us, with anything new, we will give up within three weeks. But if we can keep going for six weeks, we have the makings of a habit – something that, even if we slip for a while, we will return to because we like how it makes us feel. That's easier with a written plan of when and what you'll do. Keep it simple – start with just following these first two steps for six weeks.

Train your body to get better at burning off fat

Taking it to the next level

So now you're convinced that you should exercise. What should you do next?

This exercise plan works equally well for first-time exercisers or those returning to regular exercise. If it's too easy for you, ratchet up a gear, or jump some steps. But beware. Research has shown that there are two reasons why exercise programmes fail:

- We don't see the results we want, or
- We set our expectations too high.

It's far better to do a little and stick to it until you have the exercise habit than go nuts, join a gym, write an ambitious exercise programme and then give up completely after a couple of weeks of failure to keep to it.

Decide on your goal

If you've never exercised before, or have lapsed, please start with a modest goal. If it's ten minutes of activity a day – that's brilliant, as long as you're confident that you'll do it. Aim to visit your local pool once a week, then build up to three times a week. Aim to swim once a week and walk around the park once a week. Aim to do a yoga class on a Saturday morning.

Make your plan

You need a schedule where every week you are aiming to do a little more, a little more frequently until you are exercising for around three to four hours a week – enough to get you out of breath for most of the time. This could take a year, but don't think about that now. Stick your monthly schedule on the fridge. At first your goal should be just to stick to your weekly plan. Once you've got the hang of it, you can make your goal bigger – run round the park, enter your local fun run, cycle to the next town then cycle back.

If you are very exhausted, very unfit, have been ill or are very overweight, all you might be able to manage is walking up the stairs. Fine. Make that your goal: to walk up the stairs three times a week, then five times a week, and so on from there. Aim for cardiovascular exercise to begin with to get your heart beating, because that's the type that will give you energy fastest.

Your first four weeks

Here is the easiest programme that you can adapt to your favourite exercise:

Week 1: Walk slowly for five minutes, walk briskly for five minutes, walk slowly for five minutes. Aim to do that for three days a week.

Week 2: Aim to do the same five times a week.

Week 3: Walk slowly for ten minutes, walk briskly for ten minutes, walk slowly for ten minutes. Aim for four times a week.

Week 4: Walk slowly for five minutes, walk briskly for twenty minutes, walk slowly for five minutes. Aim for five times a week.

After this start increasing the time you walk briskly and reduce the time you take it easy.   Remember the acronym FIT: frequency, intensity, time per session. First work on frequency – aim to do some form of exercise five or six times a week. Then work on 'T' – the time you spend at it each time you do it. Then move on to the intensity – use hills to make you work harder, or go faster, or try a more difficult stroke if you're swimming.

If you are still struggling, think of hooking up with a buddy. Research proves that a friend will encourage and support you, and make it more likely that you will keep to your programme.

Once you've got the hang of it, you can make your goal bigger

Quiz:
Lost your vitality?

Lost your sparkle? Find it hard to muster a modicum of enthusiasm, energy, motivation? Here's how to get back your zing.

Blame a poor diet, too little sleep, too much work – but occasionally it does feel as though that scoundrel Life has put a slow puncture in our bubble-self and the air is seeping out, leaving us feeling like a damp, rubber blob.

And when you're feeling lacklustre, there's little chance you'll have the fervour to start that new project, launch that new business, downsize, overhaul your finances, start a new health regime. Even getting up and making yourself a cup of tea can be like climbing Kilimanjaro.

Take a few minutes to assess your vitality levels. Answer the following questions:

1. How are you in the mornings?

a) Fresh as a daisy. I'm the archetypal lark.

b) Bit jaded, but fine by mid-morning.

c) Morning? Wassat? I can't hold a conversation before midday.

2. What do you usually have for breakfast?

a) Muesli, fruit, eggs – always a nutritious one.

b) A pop tart and a cup of tea.

c) Espresso and a Malboro light.

3. What effect does exercise have on your energy levels?

a) I often find it revs me up – gives me energy.

b) I never work out if I'm tired – much rather have a nap.

c) Are you mad? I'm far too knackered to exercise!

4. Describe your décor.

a) Neutral, clean lines, bright and airy – I need space and light.

b) Bit messy, but posh wallpaper, and I've just painted the bedroom moss green.

c) I favour deep purple, dark velvets, thick curtains – think Morticia Adams meets Elle Deco.

5. You're hungry – what do you snack on?

a) Nuts, seeds and dried fruit – handy and nutritious.

b) Cheese roll from the local sarnie shop.

c) A Mars Bar and a Diet Coke.

6. You're going crazy at work and someone slaps another file on your desk – what do you do?

a) Take a stroll round the block, breathe deeply, come back and take a clean sheet – time to re-prioritise the to-do list.

b) Go into panic mode, make a stiff coffee and try to multitask, pronto.

c) Give up and go home with a migraine.

7. You've been invited to a good friend's party but feel jaded and dull. Do you:

a) Take a shower, grab your party gear and put on some music to get yourself in the mood.

b) Have a swift half and a bag of monkey nuts and hope for the best.

c) Go to bed instead. Hey, staying in gave Greta Garbo icon status…

8. You're feeling glum. How do you cheer yourself up?

a) Good friends, Frascati and a feelgood film.

b) Gloria Gaynor and a rum & coke.

c) See 2c and 5c – either. Both.

Mostly As

You are clearly not short of joie de vivre, which is great news. Capitalise on all that vitality – get up even earlier. Studies show that 5 a.m. is when our energy levels are at their most powerful – lasting 'til about 7.30, so you could get up even earlier and get more done. You're a savvy eater – you know breakfast is the most important meal of the day to eat for energy. For the ultimate power breakfast, try eggs on toast with orange juice, or a milk-based fruit smoothie with added wheatgerm. High fibre foods also ensure optimum digestion; constipation can leave you lacking in energy. And bravo on your smart snacking – choosing lean proteins and fresh fruit and veg instead of choc and crisps – means you'll stay full without adding tons of calories to your daily intake.

Mostly Bs

You're kind of on the right path to vitality, but those shortcuts you take – chocolate, booze – actually zap your energy. They may give you a short boost, but long term they're doing your body no favours. Try super-snacking. Grazing provides a constant stream of energy and helps regulate your blood sugar and means your body will be able to use the food more efficiently so you won't experience extreme highs and lows in your energy levels. And try getting outside during the day. Lack of natural light and exposure to fluorescent light (that's used in most offices) can trigger your body's production of melatonin, which can make you feel mentally and physically fatigued. Lounging in the sun over a frappucino, or going for a 20-minute walk at lunchtime can boost your vitality.

Mostly Cs.

Oh dear! It's amazing you managed to stay awake long enough to finish this quiz. Follow as many of the hints in the quiz as you can take on. Here's a simple idea you can start on right away. Ditch the sombre décor and matching attire. Instead surround yourself with bright colours – they energise you. Think bright stripes, big flowers, happy colours. Experts have found that when people are surrounded by sunny shades they feel cheerful, energised, optimistic and happy. And instead of giving up when pressures mount – get focused. At work, for example, try dividing your day into regular scheduled 30 or 60 minute slots – it can boost your productivity and refresh a cluttered mind. You'll feel in control and brighter.

Take control of your work–life balance: Get your life back

We all have so much on our plates that it can be hard to be clear about what needs to be done, what our priorities are and most importantly – when to do it all. One way of taking back control is to divide things up into categories of activities and then schedule time for the different areas. When doing this, it's really important to remember the 'buffer' activities. These are all those things that make life flow more smoothly – all the admin jobs that need to be done but you never find time for – filing receipts, dental check-ups, searching for cheaper car insurance. Take a few minutes to do this exercise.

- *Make a master list of everything you have to do.*
- *Divide the list into three categories – work, 'buffer', free time.*
- *Now take your diary and set aside at least a half day for 'buffering' per week, as many work days as you need*

and at least one day a week free time (this is reserved for total enjoyment – no guilt or duty outings, those are buffer activities). Free time is about total enjoyment.

- *Assign tasks for every work day and buffer period day of the week. Be realistic and obviously start with the most important stuff. If you can't get round to the important stuff because you have so many appointments, you need to think about curtailing meetings. Your to-do list is simply fantasy if you don't have any time to complete tasks.*
- *As you achieve each task colour it in highlighter pen.*

Now you have prioritised what you have to do, but most importantly you've found slots of time in which you can achieve it. This method also means you remember to take time off, essential for you to recharge, and also find time for 'buffering' by attending to the non-essential but important tasks that we generally ignore until they become critical.

Take control of your image: revitalise your style

To define your style, you need to know what it isn't. Learn the art of editing.

Reduce choice

Before you start de-cluttering your wardrobe, it helps
to know what image you are aiming for. It will help you
decide what to keep and what to get rid of. Any way you
can find to edit your wardrobe is recommended. For
example, you might get your 'colours' done: and then
ruthlessly throw out all the coloured clothing that is deemed
not to suit you. Another incredibly simple but incredibly
chic idea is to wear nothing but black or navy in winter
and nothing but cream or white in summer. Think of how
simple shopping and dressing would be if you kept to that
very French way of limiting choice. Or you could decide
that your signature look is always going to be tailored and
smart, so you won't waste time on those floaty skirts and
shirts that you buy, but never end up wearing.

Find your passion

This method of finding your style and editing your
wardrobe is one devised by Leslie and Susannah Kenton
and shared in their book *Authentic Woman*. Their theory
is that defining your style means letting passion guide
your clothing choices rather than reading magazines for
inspiration. You create your own style by examining what
inspires your passion.

Answer these questions:

1. Name a type of animal or bird that you love.
   What quality do you appreciate about it?
   Example: *Cat = elegant.*
2. Think of an actress in a film you love. Which of her character's qualities do you appreciate?
   Example: *Louise* in Thelma and Louise = *strength*
3. Name a flower you love. What quality does it represent?
   Example: *Rose = feminine*
4. Think of a person whom you love and admire.
   Which of their qualities do you appreciate most?
   Example: *My friend Diana who is easy going and always there for me.*
5. Think of a place in nature that you love. Why?
   Example: *The seaside, it always makes me feel alive.*

Therefore your style would be: elegant, strong but feminine, relaxed and vibrant.

Create the wardrobe for your new style

Write your style statement on post-it notes. Stick it on your wardrobe door and keep it with you when you go shopping.

Check it before you buy anything new to make sure the item fits with your style.

When it comes to throwing out clothes, bear your style statement in mind. Now you understand what image you really want to project you might understand why certain items of clothing never get worn – if you want to be sexy, it's unlikely you'll ever feel completely comfortable in those fashionable but slightly masculine brogues. Go through your whole wardrobe – every single drawer and cupboard. Touch every item once and if you don't love it, or haven't worn it for a year, or it doesn't fit in with the new image you want to project, place it into one of two piles:

The 'out' pile

It's damaged, stained, looks worn, doesn't make you feel great, doesn't fit in with the new image you want to project.

The 'needing love' pile

It could make you feel good, if it was dry-cleaned, mended, repaired or altered, or if you had another item of clothing or some shoes that would go with it.

The next step is obvious. Chuck the 'out' pile and spend some attention and money on the 'needing love' pile.

Now that everything in your wardrobe suits you and fits in with your image (including your underwear), bring order to your closets by reorganising and reordering how clothes and shoes are stored.

Knowing that your wardrobe is working for you and that everything is ordered and makes you look great, really uplifts and energises you. And because you've spent some time concentrating on the image you want to project to the world, you'll feel more confident, too. A fantastic return for a day's effort.

Create your own style by examining what inspires your passion

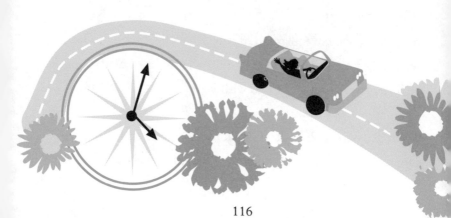

Oprah Winfrey's life management tips

The richest entertainer who has the Midas touch when it comes to business, regularly tops lists of powerful people – and still loves her job.

She is always herself

'Anything else would be too hard and I couldn't sustain it. It gets easier as you get older and it's one of the great benefits of passing decades. All your experiences are learning curves and give you the confidence to be yourself.'

She understands the relationship between money and job satisfaction

'I have a great relationship with money. Always did have even when I didn't have any. I never feared not having it and when I got it didn't obsess about keeping it. So now I've got enough that I can buy whatever I want – because the bank balance doesn't matter. I've always wanted the same feeling I got from my first job in radio – the feeling that I love this so much even if you don't pay me, I'd show up every day just to be here.'

She sees challenges as opportunities

'I know that in every challenge there's an opportunity to grow, enhance your life, or learn something invaluable about yourself. Every challenge can make you stronger if you allow it. When your life is on course with its purpose, you are your most powerful. And you may stumble. But you will not fall.'

Take control of your money: manage your debt

Credit cards are not virtual income,
they simply reflect our capacity for debt.

Here's the reality behind some financial double speak. Credit is simply another word for debt. When a credit card company increases your credit limit, what it's really saying is that you are considered to be a reliable payer of the extortionate rates of interest they charge. If you use your credit, sorry debt card as a way of seeing you over short-term cash flow that's fine. If you pay off the outstanding balance most months, fine. But if you don't, getting rid of your debt will save you a fortune.

- If there is any way you can pay outright without using a card, do so. If the only way you can afford something is to pay by credit card, think very carefully before buying it.
- Always try to pay off 10% of your balance every month on your credit cards – if you only pay the minimum it will cost you loads and take an age to clear.
- Do not, whatever you do, build up the amount you owe on store cards. With one or two exceptions, their annual interest rates are extremely high.
- Used intelligently credit cards can be useful sources of free credit. Used rashly, they can bring about an imperceptible slide into long-term debt.
- If you have multiple credit cards, identify which one has the most draconian interest rate and shred it. Don't

tuck it in a drawer and rely on your willpower not to use it. Experience suggests this is not a great tactic.

- Talk to your creditors and let them know if you are having problems. Work out how much you can realistically afford to pay. Focus on the most important monthly payments – mortgage, council tax, gas, electricity, etc.
- Don't panic but don't ignore the problem.
- Don't pay for advice. There are plenty of sources of free help and counselling. Talk to your bank, or the Citizen's Advice Bureau.

Getting rid of your debt will save you a fortune

Save before spending

If you find it difficult or impossible to save money, here's an approach that will enable you to divert some of your monthly discretionary spend into a savings account.

Building up your savings is a very good thing to do and an excellent habit to get into. And not least because we all find our wallets or purses ambushed at short notice by sizeable bills coming out of left field at us. As well as warding off emergencies, savings can enable us to plan for the future, it might even be something coming up relatively soon – your next holiday, upgrading the computer or replacing the car.

Don't get suckered into a 'not today, maybe tomorrow' attitude to saving. Set up a standing order from your current to your savings account and make sure it goes out early in the month. (Wait until the end and you may well find that you've no money left.) Make it a reasonable amount but critically one that you can afford. To help avoid any temptation to dip into your savings, set up the savings account so that the money you've saved isn't too readily accessible. Use the building society across town rather than the one around the corner, and consider going for an account where you have to give notice before you can make a withdrawal. Set aside a certain amount each month as savings, and then make the remainder your budget for the month.

Is this possible? Yes, when you consider that on average around 20% of household expenditure goes on leisure.

Think of the thousands each year that we fritter away on lattes, newspapers and magazines, pricey sandwiches, DVDs, chocolate and so on.

If you don't have a savings mentality try setting yourself a goal. It might be to have three to six months' salary set aside for emergencies or to have a new TV in twelve months that you can pay for outright. Whatever you plump for, having a goal gives a bit of meaning and purpose to the idea of saving. It comes in handy when you next walk past Starbucks to remind yourself that passing on that take-out coffee is not just wilful self-denial it's helping to bring that huge screen closer to you.

Having a goal gives a bit of meaning and purpose to the idea of saving

Feel good now: *'There are few problems that can't be solved by spending ten minutes or so alone in the peace and quiet. Many of us are under so much pressure today, we seldom set aside time for ourselves. But the truth is, living as we do in a 24 hour society, and a materialistic one at that, can take its toll on our health and emotional well-being if we don't keep it in check.'* Fiona Harrold, life coach (www.fionaharrold.com)

Four

Revitalise your
relationships

Nothing is going to make your life flow more
smoothly than supportive, loving relationships.
Nothing is going to convince you faster that you
are on the right track than being surrounded
by love. It's time to focus on relationships,
including the all-important one with yourself.

Quiz:
Are your relationships in good shape?

Relationships form the scaffolding of our lives. They can be the source of our greatest joy, offering us security, laughter and love. Or they can bring us down faster than a lift in freefall.

Here's a quick questionnaire to help you assess whether or not your relationships need a bit of TLC – or major surgery.

To what extent do you agree with the following statements – agree (score 3), disagree (score 1), not sure (score 2).

1. I like myself – I approve of myself – I'm pretty confident I'm a good person to be around.

2. Variety is the key to healthy relationships – you can't expect one person to satisfy every single emotional need – otherwise that relationship is doomed to failure.

3. Arguing can be a positive element to a relationship – fighting can be good if it's constructive.

4. I'm happy to apologise when I'm wrong.

5. I accept that as life changes and people find partners, get married and have children, I can't always spend the same amount of time with my friends. But I can ensure a good relationship with them.

6. I have reached a place of acceptance and forgiveness with my parents and others in my life for their mistakes. I don't blame them, or get angry with them, or allow myself to be made to feel bad by them.

7. I don't have any problem praising others in public or telling them I love them.

8. When I communicate with people I'm specific rather than vague. It gets better responses.

9. I know when to shut up and I wouldn't tackle relationship problems when I'm tired; I know when to protect myself.

10. My partner and I love being together, but we enjoy our private space too – weekends away, nights out apart – it makes our time together more intense.

11. I regularly compliment other people – and myself (even if it's only me that knows it).

12. I can honestly say I don't try to change my partner, or others.

13. I'm confident and open when meeting people for the first time.

14. I don't waste my time constantly worrying about living up to other people's expectations. I apologise if I get it wrong but otherwise accept that I am me and that's enough.

15. I'm an optimist.

Scored 36–45

Sounds like you have a very healthy approach to relationships – optimistic, but realistic too, and mature enough to know that they need good careful maintenance. You're a grown up who realises that sound communication is the cornerstone of a healthy relationship. You also realise that being your own best friend is the first step towards having strong bonds and partnerships. Experts say that other people's behaviour towards us tends to mirror the feelings we have about ourselves, and your feelings are healthy and strong.

Scored 16–35

You have a pretty healthy approach to relationships, although you may have moments of jealousy and insecurity, and perhaps roll out your bottom lip when things aren't going your way. If you're going to get the hump, at least learn to argue constructively. Relationships expert Dr Judy Kurianksy, author of *The Complete Idiot's Guide to A Healthy Relationship* recommends these fighting fair rules. Stick to the present ('this time, you did...'), make agreements (ask yourself what can be resolved), concentrate on the *act* not the person, give details, be fully attentive to your opponent and try to see their point of view ('I can understand that...') See? This way you're so much more likely to create a positive outcome and oil the wheels of communication.

Scored 0–15

Oh dear! Chances are you're adept at shedding friends and partners by the busload. So what goes wrong? Experts recommend doing a relationship post-mortem so you can learn lessons along the way. Ask yourself some questions. What would I have needed in order to choose a more suitable partner? How could I have started the relationship better and laid down more structured ground rules? When things started to go wrong, what could I have done differently? And remember this: don't crave anyone so much that you trick yourself into thinking you won't survive without them. You will. Remember, you're as attractive/happy/ special as you think you are. Treat yourself as gorgeous and others will follow your lead.

Improve your relationships in seconds

Most of us know how important relationships are yet we tend to take them for granted. But it doesn't take much to make your loved ones feel like VIPs…

If you were in a crisis tomorrow, would you have ample people to call on? If you wanted to have fun, could you throw a spontaneous party certain that your friends would turn up and make the evening memorable? How healthy are your relationships – with family, friends, colleagues, your partner – and let's not forget, yourself? If the answer to that is, 'mmm, a bit under the weather', the chances are you need to give them some emergency tlc.

One UK survey showed that nearly 48% of us believe that relationships are the biggest factor in making us happy. So far so good. However, apparently one in twenty-five of us speak to no friends at all in an average week.

The clue is in the last sentence. All you need to do is talk and you don't have to talk that long. By investing time in your relationships with your partner, friends and family, and widening your social circle you'll garner support to help you cope through the difficult times, and have the chance to relax and have fun. It's also a far better insurance against having a happy future than a healthy pension given the latest financial storms – and a whole lot easier to guarantee.

Four ways to improve your relationships

1. Switch off the TV. It will give you time to connect with your partner and your children, and allow you to get back in touch with people (see below).

2. Make a list of all those people you want to call. Set aside 10 minutes to call a friend or relative who is on your conscience. If you did this every evening you would soon get the reputation for being the most attentive friend in the world. Pick people who make you feel good. And when you have called all of them, turn to those who are on your conscience. If you are dreading the call, work out why. Worried it will take hours? Don't let it; preface the conversation with a 'just thinking about you and felt I had to call before I go out'. That puts restrictions on the time the call lasts. Do they 'guilt you out'? Why? Tell yourself firmly that you are doing your best for them at the moment and even if this isn't strictly true, ignoring them will only make you feel worse. Do they always bring you down? Again, work out why. Deal with your issues on this and, again, restrict time spent on the call.

3. Pay everyone you love that you meet today a heartfelt compliment. Make it about their general character and also be specific. 'I love the fact that you are so

thoughtful. Look at the way you've tidied your room.'
'I am so lucky to live with someone as funny as you.
I was feeling fed up but your lunchtime text made
my day.'

4. Spend 10 minutes with each of your children doing
   exactly what they want to do and giving them your total
   attention. In fact, this is good advice for anyone in
   your life.

*All you need to do is talk
and you don't have to talk
that long*

Re-energise a bad relationship

Going through a bad period in your relationship when you are finding it hard to get on? Here are some new perspectives.

These techniques can help turn around the way you feel about a partner who is being a pain in the neck. They are based on getting a new look at the situation so you don't keep repeating the same patterns of behaviour over and over again. (For instance: he snaps, you get angry, he withdraws.) The old saying is true: you can't change anyone else, you can only change yourself. But by changing the way you respond to a situation, you can dramatically change the dynamics of it. You may find that your partner begins to respond to you more positively but at the very least you will feel better about yourself.

See your partner as a mirror

When your partner is acting badly, look at it from this point of view: their behaviour is a mirror image of you. You know the phrase, when you point a finger, the thumb is pointing back at you. That's what is meant. Whatever you don't like or can't accept in your partner is a reflection of some aspect of yourself that you don't like. At first this sounds ridiculous. But couples mirror each other all the time (and can even trigger in their partner the attitudes that in themselves they find unacceptable, a phenomenon known as 'projection' where, for instance, partner A continually provokes partner B to lose their temper because A has problems dealing with conflict or anger themselves).

So think of it this way. Your partner's behaviour can be seen as a spiritual guide to what you need to fix in yourself. Suppose he is being withdrawn and silent? Look to the bit in you that isn't being honest, truthful, transparent and spoken, with him and with others. You don't trust a word he says because he keeps lying? Where are you lying to yourself? When you start being more honest with yourself, your partner may well begin to be more honest with you, mirroring back your behaviour. When you are more outgoing, they become keener to spend time with you. Realising the impact that looking at ourselves has on others has a very powerful effect on our lives.

See your partner as a teacher

The trouble is that when relationships go sour, it often brings out the worst in us – neediness, anger, vindictiveness. Instead, use this as an opportunity to nurture your best qualities. What qualities do you need to put up with their nonsense? Charm? Tolerance? Assertiveness? See yourself as this charming, tolerant, assertive person and start 'acting up' to the role. Remember the saying 'what doesn't kill you, makes you stronger' – this is it in action. Allowing your best qualities to bloom under your partner's pressure means that you will think better of yourself and your self-esteem will rise. It is a win-win situation for you whatever they do.

See your partner as hurting

A Tao master would say that when someone is hurting you, they are in pain and asking for your help – it's the old mirroring thing again. (Of course, if they are hurting you physically, you need to remove yourself from the vicinity.) Think of their bad behaviour as a cry for help. What's the cry for? What are they looking for from you that you are not providing? Usually it's compassion or appreciation. Try extending understanding and empathy to them and see if it makes a difference to the way they treat you.

See your relationship as a choice, not a curse

Ultimately, if your relationship is bad, you can leave. So if you stay, it means you're in it because you choose to be there. Realising that we are choosing a situation, rather than having it forced upon us, can be incredibly liberating. When a relationship is framed as a choice not an endurance test, we tend to take responsibility for improving it rather than retreating into blame and recrimination. This change in attitude can effect a big change for the better.

You can't change anyone else, you can only change yourself

Connect and stay connected

It doesn't take much to keep in connection with your partner, but it's amazing how many of us don't manage even that.

Read, digest and ponder. Then get your diary, a big red pen and start prioritising your relationship. Below are the three golden rules of a healthy relationship. All the technique and creativity in the world isn't going to fix a relationship where the couple aren't properly together. On the other hand, couples who spend time together and anticipate and plan for those times, find it hard to lose interest in one another.

Rule 1. Daily…

How is your partner feeling right now? What's happening at work? How are their relationships with friends, colleagues, siblings, parents? Carve out 15 minutes every day to talk. If you find yourselves getting into a rut of busyness, when you pass like ships in the night for several days in a row without touching base, either go to bed before your usual time or get up earlier and have a coffee together so you can reconnect.

Kiss each other every morning before you get out of bed. Take the time for a cuddle. Breathe deeply. Hold tight. Do the same at night. Never take your physical intimacy for granted. You found each other. This is worth acknowledging with at least a daily hug.

Rule 2. Weekly...

Go out with each other once a week when humanly possible – once a fortnight is the bare minimum. According to the experts, this is the most important thing you can do. Couples who keep dating, keep mating. Spending too long sloping around the same house does something to a couple's sexual interest in each other and what it does generally isn't good. So get out, preferably after making some small effort to tart yourself up so you're visually pleasing to your partner. Let them see why they bothered with you in the first place. (This isn't rocket science, but it works.)

Rule 3. Monthly...

Go for a mini-adventure – shared memories cement a relationship. Make your adventure as mad or staid as you like, but at the very least make sure it's something that you haven't done since the beginning of your relationship. It really doesn't matter what it is, as long as it's not your usual 'date'.

What's the point? You see your partner coping with new environments and new skills and that keeps you interested in them. And them in you.

If you're shaking your head and thinking 'how banal', that could be a mistake. Research shows that the difference between strong couples and 'drifting' couples is the amount of effort and time they spend on their shared pursuits. All of us have heard the advice 'spend more time with each other, being as interesting as possible.' But how many couples do you know who actually do it? And what's the betting, they are the happiest.

Never take your physical intimacy for granted

Communicate clearly

Try these tips from www.shrinkwrap.com

1. *Use 'I' and 'me' not 'you'.*

2. *Check your assumptions with the person you're talking to. You're probably wrong.*

3. *Have one argument at a time. Stick to the present and don't bring up old stuff.*

4. *Aim for a win-win which means both of you get something. Give to get.*

5. *For a win-win to happen you have to know what you want. What do you want to achieve?*

6. *Try requesting and appreciating rather than criticising and complaining.*

Give your love life a boost

When you want to feel in the mood, try this.

You may be going through a quiet patch in your love life but that doesn't mean you have to go through Relate to get yourself back on track. Working on the theory, and indeed the fact, that the more we think about sex, the more we want it, this is a one-week plan that forces you to think about sex just a little bit more. Prioritising it in your mind will make you feel sexier and jolt you out of your take it or leave it stance. You don't have to actually be with your partner for the magic to work. You've just got to consciously think about sex a little more.

Remember you don't have to believe in it for it to work, just do it.

Seven days to feel a whole lot sexier

Monday – hop into the shower together

You may not have time to act on it, but getting lathered up together will get you thinking about sex, and that's a start.

Tuesday – have breakfast in the garden

University of California research shows that libido is increased by 69% if you spend an hour a day outside.

Wednesday – buy apple strudel for dinner

Or any pudding that's got cinnamon in it. The smell is

such an aphrodisiac that it increases the flow of blood to the bits that matter.

Thursday – text your partner

Couples need to keep touching to release regular doses of oxytocin, the bonding hormone. When you're away, 'virtual' strokes – with saucy or romantic texts – work nearly as well.

Friday – order garlic bread with lunch

Garlic contains allicin, which increases blood flow to the genitals and thus improves sensation and orgasm. Aim to eat a bulb crushed into food each week.

Saturday – do the shopping

Have a look at some women's sex aid sites. Even if you're not buying, browsing will get you thinking. And that's all you need.

Sunday – turn up the central heating

'Surprise' your partner by walking around naked when they least expect it. It will give them a shock and that will get them out of any of their doldrums.

It is self-evident that by thinking about sex more you're going to be more likely to be in the mood that night. Someone who is thinking about chores, work, and all they have to do the next day is naturally not going to be as up for sex as someone who has allowed a few frisky thoughts to interrupt their routine. 'Making it different' is another simple way to keep it fresh between you. Try sleeping in front of the fire, in a tent in the garden, in the spare room. A little willingness to experiment can work wonders on your sexual energy levels.

Choosing a cinnamon pastry is not going to send your hormones haywire but now you know about cinnamon every time you choose it you're thinking that this is a conscious decision to get a little bit sexier. And that conscious decision could well affect your libido.

By all means ignore all of the above, as long as you substitute your own methods of surprising your partner and thinking about sex more often.

Consciously think about sex a little more

Get everyone on your side

We all want to steer people towards our way of thinking. So what's the most effective way of influencing people?

When we want people to follow our lead, we usually try to find as many different ways to get our thoughts across as possible. If someone disagrees, we just try to come at it another way. However, does this actually work?

Picture a pile of sand. If you pour a jug of water over the sand, it's likely that some of it will be soaked up by the sand and that some of it will trickle down the edge of the pile making pathways as it goes. If you pour another jug of water on the same pile of sand, more may soak in and some may make new pathways. Most of it however, is likely to travel down the original pathways and make these deeper. If you pour yet another jug of water over the sand it will be virtually impossible for the water to do anything other than go down the existing pathways, making them deeper than ever.

This is almost exactly how the brain works. When you give someone a problem to solve they'll begin to think it through and pathways or traces will be created through the brain. You tell them you think they've got it wrong and they need to think it through again. This they do and they may possibly find a new pathway, making that idea deeper or more firmly entrenched. Ask them to think it through again and it'll be almost impossible for them to come up with a new solution. It's not that they don't want to – it's just that the pathways have now been created and the brain finds it virtually impossible to move away from those pathways.

When you look at this picture it's obvious that continually trying to change someone's mind by telling them, yet again, why you think the way you do, is likely to be less than useless.

We all have a perception of the way we communicate. Most of us think we are open to ideas, that we show caring to others and that we encourage others to come forward with their thoughts and suggestions. But if their style of communication is measured, most people are shocked by the results. We absolutely do not communicate the way we think we do.

Without even realising it, we usually communicate by giving our point of view, giving our suggestions and telling people why we don't agree with their ideas. What we don't do is support their ideas, ask for their opinions, test our understanding of what they're saying, summarise all their points of view, or take their ideas and demonstrate their value by building on them. We don't invite them into the conversation. In the first way, all our focus is on 'I'; in the second it's all on 'you'. For the duration of your very next conversation, try not to use the word 'I'. Concentrate entirely on 'you'. Ask 'you' questions. What do you think about this? How might you handle this? Let me test what you are saying to be sure that I've understood you correctly. That is a great idea that you have just had. This way you'll see how much more people are able to contribute. You'll also notice how difficult you'll find it to not take over and voice your ideas.

If you really want to influence people the knack is to ask questions that allow them the opportunity to think about something in a different way. In other words, allow the brain to come from a different starting point. First, focus on helping them explore their idea. Then focus on developing their idea to incorporate yours.

The brain finds it virtually impossible to move away from those pathways

10 ways to nurture yourself

1. Book a massage or facial

2. Set aside a couple of hours to watch a favourite movie

3. Lie on the couch and listen to an audio book or a CD properly

4. Go on what writer Julia Cameron calls 'an artist's date' and take a couple of hours to pursue some event or place that you are interested in. Look for spurts of creative interest that you can follow up.

5. Sit quietly with an open page and a pen. Write freely. You may be surprised at what comes up.

6. Spend the morning in bed

7. Go to bed at 9 p.m.

8. Spend the morning in a local spa or sports centre enjoying a steam, sauna and swim

9. Treat yourself to new bed linen

10. Redecorate your bedroom

Love yourself

Because without you, you're nothing.

Michelle Obama has talked about the 'epiphany' in her relationship with her husband when she realised that if she wanted to be happy, she had to look after herself. This includes exercising at 4.30 a.m. People discuss this as if it's proof that Mrs Obama is some sort of self-control freak but as she has said 'if my children need caring for at 4 in the morning, I get up. So why shouldn't I get up at 4 to look after myself.'

Women are built to nurture. Even when we're stressed, we release the hormone oxytocin which encourages us to nurture more. Little surprise that so many of us find ourselves stressed out and wrung out, but still on a treadmill of endlessly running chores for others while neglecting ourselves. Turning this around means forgetting the training of a lifetime.

*Actions not words
are what count*

Lavish some attention on yourself

How do you show your love for others? Buy food and cook it deliciously? Clean up after them? Show interest in their lives? Write thank you notes? Offer gifts? Hug them close even when they are being annoying?

Look at the events you have planned over the next month and think about how you'll be showing love through your plans. For instance:

- I'll be taking flowers when visiting a relative to show I care about them. (What about giving yourself flowers?)
- I'll be throwing a dinner party and cooking a delicious meal for my friends to enjoy. (When did you last consider what you most wanted to eat, went out and bought the ingredients and cooked for yourself with no thoughts about others' needs?)
- I'll be taking my children to a pantomime as a special treat. (Where would you like to go? What show would thrill you?)

You get the idea. You show love every day towards others. How about expending a fraction of that attention on yourself. You are just as deserving of love as anyone else but actions not words are what count. Many of us, although we recognise the intellectual truth of our worthiness, act more like an enemy towards ourselves than a loving friend.

Feel good now: *'It's vital to get off the treadmill occasionally. I always recommend this useful exercise: choose a time to shut yourself away for 15 minutes with a pen and paper, and plan how to make small adjustments to your life. It can help make an enormous difference to your happiness and satisfaction levels.'* Fiona Harrold, life coach (www.fionaharrold.com)

Michelle Obama's life management tips

The First Lady is arguably more successful than her husband. How do you get to be a First Lady of substance?

She knows she has to put herself first sometimes if she wants to function optimally 'I was mad with Barack after our second child was born. I am sitting there at 4 in the morning feeding our baby, tired, angry, out of shape – and he's asleep. That's when it struck me that if I wasn't there, he'd have to do it. I started going to the gym early in the morning and when I came home, the girls were dressed and fed.'

She works on her support network

'I needed support but not necessarily from Barack. We all need community in our lives. But it is difficult to create it if you are unable to sustain meaningful relationships with other women. We have to champion other women. If there is anyone who has a broken relationship with another woman, if there is a woman that you are not communicating with because of ego, or jealousy or fear of rejection, a sister or a friend or a mother or a child who could be part of your community, I recommend you reach out.'

She takes care of her body when she's under stress

'Changing your diet, eliminating artificial ingredients and eating with the seasons, gives you more energy. It's what we did when Barack decided to run for senior office and it made a big difference.'

Be irresistible

The ability to draw others towards you
effortlessly is a great gift and one that will make
your life flow very much more easily.

The secret of magnetism is twofold – a sense of being grounded and happy in your own skin coupled with the assurance that you are someone worth knowing. This quality makes life a lot easier. Life seems to flow towards you effortlessly. That's what the father of life coaching, US guru, Thomas Leonard called 'irresistible attraction'. Which is a fabulous way of saying 'sky-high self-esteem'.

Without self-esteem, at best you feel insecure, at worst you feel helpless, depressed, isolated. Life seems difficult if you don't feel other people care about you enough. However, self-esteem is not set in stone. It fluctuates depending on what is going on in our lives. Keeping an eye on our self-esteem and shoring it up when it is going through a dip is time well spent.

Answer yes or no to these statements based on how you're feeling now, today – not how you felt last week, last year or last millennium.

1. Does life seem unnecessarily complicated?
2. Do all your attempts to make life better seem to get stuck?
3. Do you feel you're at the mercy of your family, job or other people?

4. Are you feeling slightly sick at the thought of all you have to achieve by the end of the week?

5. Do you feel that if you want something you can make it happen?

6. Do you feel that you are expressing who you really are through your image, home, work or interests?

Answer no to the first four questions and yes to questions 5 and 6, and you can skip this idea – for now. Yes to the first four questions; no to questions 5 or 6 and your self-esteem could use some work. The good news is you can start right now. You'll have higher self-esteem by the time you go to bed tonight.

Make a difference – it makes you gloriously attractive

One characteristic of people with low self-esteem is that, deep down, they don't think it matters if they exist or not. Those with healthy self-esteem know why they make a difference to the world. Easiest way of doing it? Pay a genuine compliment and then 'big' it up. Tell the bloke who makes your coffee how good it is, and let his manager overhear. Compliment your assistant on a job well done, and then email your boss to let her know about his good work. Paying compliments makes you powerful. You remember the person who gave you a heartfelt compliment for the rest of your life. Don't you want to be that kind of memorable person?

Ditch the martyrdom – it's deeply unattractive

All of us do things we don't want to do, but some of us get caught in a trap of working to other people's agendas too much of the time. Think of one chore you really don't want to do: visit your aunt, help at the school fete, paint the bedroom. Now remember – it's optional. Pretty much everything in life is. Cancel it and do something that makes you happy instead. When 'duty' tasks mount up we feel overwhelmed and out of control. Saying no means you start to question every single time you say yes. Saying no to other people and yes to yourself is very liberating.

Two ways to work on your self esteem

1. Write down 50 words you would like to apply to yourself; joyful, optimistic, strong, intuitive, confident. Now taking each word in turn, say out loud 'I am...' How true does that sound to you? If it's very true, score 2; moderately, score 1; not at all, score 0. Look at the 2s. Affirm those positive feelings. Look at the others. Imagine how you'd be if you had scored 2 on them. Now pick a couple and try to 'act as if'. This is

incredibly powerful and the basis of the behavioural therapy NLP (neuro linguistic programming). Think how you would behave, look and act if you were a strong, optimistic, or joyful person – and then do it! One day you'll find you're not acting.

2. Set aside half an hour and write down every single thing you've been successful at or that you've completed successfully. You can put anything on the list as long as it's meaningful to you. Finding a good dentist could be as much of a success as getting a promotion at work. When you run out of steam, look over the list and write down the qualities you needed to achieve each success: perseverance, courage, quick wit. Return to this list until you have at least 100 successes and then give yourself a really nice reward for being so successful.

Paying compliments makes you powerful

Index